MW00627422

Boot Camp
for the

Soul

LISA LAMONT

BOOK PUBLISHERS NETWORK

Book Publishers Network
P.O. Box 2256
Bothell • WA • 98041
Ph • 425-483-3040
www.bookpublishersnetwork.com

10 9 8 7 6 5 4 3 2 1

Printed in the United States of America

LCCN   2011936655
ISBN   978-1-937454-02-9

Editor: Julie Scandora
Cover designer: Laura Zugzda
Typographer: Stephanie Martindale
Prancing Kitten Logo: Karyn Rasmussen

To protect the privacy of my clients, I have changed their names and some details of their stories.

To my daughters, Michelle and Whitney, for always believing in their mom. And to my love, Jeff Olsen, who loves to watch me prance.

Contents

Acknowledgments

Scott Gilbert, PhD, who treats me as an equal and shows that we are never too old to change careers.

Carolyn Kelly, former president and CEO of the *Seattle Times*, an amazing woman who "walks the talk."

My talented editor, Julie Scandora, who created this book out of my jumbled thoughts.

Doug Brown, president and CEO of All Star Directories, who took the time in his hectic schedule to share with me the importance of staying out of the box.

Preface

Desperate to get control over their weight, women seek me out in my practice as a hypnotherapist. They have struggled with diets over the years, only to fail time and again. I know their situation all too well for I, too, once carried fifty extra pounds and tried one diet after another, looking for the one that would magically fix me.

Finally, I realized I was searching for the solution in the wrong place—out there—rather than within. I wanted something or someone else to take care of my weight problem—tell me what to eat, provide me with well-balanced, packaged meals, lead me in appropriate exercises, etc. Sure, I'd be the one eating or jogging, but all those programs came from outside of me, proven in the payments I made to join the programs.

But once I went inside and learned to love Lisa, the pounds slipped away.

Too easy, you say? Not at all. Simple, yes, but loving me took far more effort than any diet I ever tried.

My clients and I consistently demonstrated that diets don't keep the pounds off in the long run. And I bet you know exactly what I mean. But now, they and I are walking proof that loving oneself does work—from the very start and from then on.

The process I will show you requires minimal time and money. But because you'll face some emotional challenges in going this route, I'm here to help you.

The result? A more beautiful you, a more loving you, a more joyful you.

Let's begin.

Introduction

QUEEN OF THE SCREEN, DIVA OF DIETS

I love Oprah. Over the years, I picked up many ideas from her guests, she inspired me, and I admired her genuine desire to help others through her show.

And yet … this awesome woman of power, one of the richest women in the world, one whose word could shoot any product to the stratosphere in sales, was fighting the battle of the bulge down in the trenches with the rest of us. Despite her wealth and access to personal trainers, private chefs, and an amazing support system, her weight problem remains. And her search for the magic solution continues. Every time she thinks she's found it because the pounds have fallen off, the power of Oprah makes that diet or trainer or routine an overnight success as thousands of women rush to copy her.

And they do, but not in the ways they expect. Like Oprah, they may lose some pounds. But like Oprah, they'll gain them back—plus a few more. And like Oprah, they'll look for the next solution that will really, truly, finally work.

I know because I did exactly that. As a fan of Oprah, I joined women across America in listening to our mentor. I, too, was tired of being overweight (again). I appreciated that Oprah had done the legwork to find the system that worked (again). I followed the program (again) and lost the pounds (again) … and then put them back on (again).

Dangers of Dieting

Obviously, this does not work. In addition, this yo-yo dieting puts our body at risk for serious health problems. These dangers include liver problems, loss of muscle, lower metabolism, heart disease, high blood pressure, stroke, diabetes, cancer, and a shortened life span.

These programs do not work for one primary reason: They do not address the real problem. Excess weight is a problem, but it merely reflects an under-lying issue that we tend to ignore. And as long as that deeper one remains unresolved, it will continue to manifest as obesity or some other life-negating habit—alcoholism, indulgence in drugs (prescriptive or illegal), cutting, spending beyond one's means, etc.

This well-kept secret allows the diet industry to succeed to the tune of billions of dollars in sales each year (fifty-eight billion dollars in 2007). And it will continue to do so, thanks to desperate and clueless women across America. What an ideal situation for diet companies! Their products won't work for more than a tiny minority of consumers, but people will buy them anyway. Anyway! For what other product do we tolerate such miserable results?

Rather than seeing a reduction in obesity, we are seeing an increase in both the numbers of those overweight and the average weight of Americans. The National Center for health statistics recently found 34 percent of Americans are clinically obese. Nearly two-thirds of Americans are overweight or obese.

Diets don't work, and beyond the medical danger in flip-flopping of weight associated with them, they pose further health risks. Diet products on the market today are dietary supplements. Under the DSHEA, or Dietary Supplement and Health Education Act, passed by Congress in 1994, the law doesn't require the manufacturers of dietary supplements to test for safety or efficacy. Think twice: You have only one body. Why would you want to put something in it that, down the road, may prove harmful to your health?

NEVER GOOD ENOUGH

Rather than address the underlying problem of obesity, the diet industry actually feeds it.

Our lack of self-love results in behavior that supports our perception of being unlovable. We humans act quite logically. If we believe something about ourselves, we act in accordance with that belief. If we believe we are honest, we will tell the truth. If we tell ourselves that we always forget people's names, we will forget the name of the person we've just met. And if we don't love ourselves, then we will behave consistent with that lack of love by engaging in self-destructive activities or making mistakes we ordinarily would not make or looking less than our best (overweight, sloppily dressed, unkempt), all of which say we are not worthy of love.

The diet industry reminds us of our unlovableness. We do not look good enough, do not meet certain standards.

This general idea that we do not measure up compared to others pervades our society and, especially, our advertising. Women fashion models, today, average five feet nine inches and 114 pounds. That reflects neither the average American woman nor the proportions for a healthy body. Clearly, the diet industry is not working toward our greater goal of having healthy bodies.

The diet industry can succeed only by selling its products and services. It remains a viable industry only by selling more each succeeding year. That means it succeeds only if its products fail. After all, if the product worked and the consumer lost the weight, why would a person continue to use it or go to another company and try a different diet product? Convincing the public that its products will help in weight reduction, despite evidence to the contrary, then becomes its primary goal.

Advertising to the rescue! A few successful dieters can keep the myth alive that a company's diet will work. And before-and-after photos will instill hope in those who desperately want to believe they can purchase the solution to their weight problem.

Such ads play on our insecurities of not being good enough on the outside—in how we look, in what we wear, in what we own. But those externalities have no meaning. Or, rather, they mean only what we believe they mean. We can wear the latest fashion, drive the slickest car, have the perfectly formed body, and still feel not good enough. With those things, insecurities can continue to haunt us; having the best of anything makes no guarantee that we'll feel good about ourselves and full of self-love.

Excess weight does contribute to an unhealthy—and, often, shortened—life. The diet industry has that right. But it fails to get to the root of the problem. Losing weight and looking great on the outside without addressing the real problem makes a temporary fix at best. It's like weeding a yard by cutting off the dandelion heads. They'll pop back up in no time. Even removing the leaves makes a difference of only a week or two before the flowers push up again. That persistent root will continue to make an appearance above ground in some way. To get rid of the dandelion, you have to dig deep and remove the whole root.

Likewise, to solve our weight problem once and for all, we must dig deep and address what truly contributes to it.

I know. I did.

Loving Lisa

I worked seven years at my last position for a law firm, and the last two years almost did me in. Changes in upper management resulted in unusually stressful conditions, and I put on more than fifty pounds in that time.

Concerns about weight had surrounded me since childhood. My mother had worried about her mother's weight. And, when I was young, after my grandmother died and then my mother's brother at age forty-two died, she became obsessed with weight, not only for herself but also for those around her, including me. As an adult, I would put on ten pounds and run into my mother, and she would ask me how much I weighed. That was the focal point of all our adult conversations. The next thing I knew, I was passing what my mother had taught me onto my children. For most of my adult life, I dwelled on my weight. Even my daughters have said that they grew up with my always talking about being on a diet or needing to lose weight. So now, at fifty-two, I finally understand that I let my obsession with weight control my life and influence my own children. In fact, my youngest daughter, Whitney, as a young teenager struggled with bulimia.

Predictably, I played the yo-yo weight game many times.

And I had issues. I was married with two daughters, a career, a home, but I was living in denial. I found myself so busy taking care of everyone else that I did not have the time to focus on me. After all, I was the wife, mom, employee, caretaker, and there was no time even to think about myself. Wouldn't that be selfish? I had so many things on my plate that I was expected to do first. Lisa came last, if time permitted. I had left my childhood and youth far behind. Adulthood for me meant taking responsibility for others until—if I lasted long enough—retirement. Life was not about Lisa.

Nor did I attend to my relationship with my husband. Not surprisingly, my marriage, though legally intact, had had nothing holding it together for a very long time. In 2006, reality hit me hard. At forty-nine, I had no marriage and no money. My former husband had thought day trading was an easy way to get rich quick, but like many others who found out the hard way, it was not. We had nothing. I had lost my home, my identity, and everything I thought had been safely tucked away.

Reality hurt. So to compensate, I welcomed denial in as my best friend. I put on my mask and acted as if I were a survivor. Nothing was going to keep me down.

At first, for the most part, this strategy worked. I had a good job, found a younger boyfriend, got a cute place to live in Seattle close to my work. My friends and family supported me. I would be just fine.

Fast forward two years. I was fifty pounds heavier, my job was miserable, and I was living with the boyfriend with whom I knew I had no future. What was I thinking? So I did what I thought would be the best thing. I moved out from the boyfriend and quickly took up with another man who said all the right things, even though my gut feeling said otherwise.

Meanwhile, I had lost some of the weight but somehow never seemed to get the last twenty pounds off. I was in a new role as a girlfriend and molding myself into someone I was not comfortable with. To make matters worse, my job—my only stability—was now in jeopardy as a new manager began cleaning house through reorganization. It didn't take a rocket scientist to know we all were wearing a huge target on our backs when he required we read a book called *Execution* before he even started his new role as our boss.

One year later, I was single yet again and this time unemployed. Having left an abusive relationship, I now found myself moving in with my daughter and her family. This was not supposed to be how life went. At fifty-one, I was supposed to be a few years away from retirement, with my home nearly paid for, and winding down from a solid career. What happened? Where did my life go? I did all the things that I thought I was supposed to do, so what was wrong with me?

The answer, I finally found, was in the mirror, looking directly back at me. In a sense, I was what was wrong. Lisa. But not exactly. Truly, I was just fine, but how I saw myself was wrong. Like Dorothy in the *Wizard of Oz*, wanting to return home and never realizing that she already had the solution to her return right with her in those ruby red shoes, I held the solution to my problems—weight as well as the others—right within me. I didn't have any special shoes to get me to my home of safety, but I did have the means to return. I had only to look into the mirror to get the answers I was looking for.

I did the work then that I will share with you. And I thought I had done all I needed to. But like removing just part of the dandelion root, I had left some part of my problems untouched. A recent high school reunion let me know I still harbored feelings of inadequacy. I really hadn't let go of all of my past and the emotions I had dealt with growing up. To heal completely, to fully love myself, I needed to dig a little deeper.

Some former classmates had organized a reunion over dinner for several of our classes. I was excited to meet classmates whom I had found on Facebook and hadn't seen in years. Still, shock struck me when I was standing in line to check in and I heard a male voice say, "Lisa Lamont."

I looked in the direction the voice had come from. Pointing to his name tag, Jeff then said his name, and I realized I was standing with one of the popular boys from high school. At that very moment, my heart started to flutter as it had thirty-plus years earlier, and I faced a guy I had never dreamed of going out with. My mind flooded back to recall what he must have thought of me back in high school—a tall, skinny girl who wore pigtails and no make-up and preferred to wear overalls rather than a dress. I found myself suddenly nervous and excited at the same time.

We found ourselves talking to each other most of the night while interacting with our former classmates.

Months later, Jeff and I are still together, enjoying life to its fullest. But it wasn't easy for me. My past and how I felt about myself almost ended our relationship before it began. I never thought that my insecurities from being teased by other boys I went to school with—calling me "chicken legs" because I was tall and skinny—would affect my relationship with Jeff. After all, he was not one of the boys who had taunted me growing up. In fact, Jeff had never said anything to me. Yet, remembering what others had said and what I had thought about myself, I found difficulty in understanding how he could love me now. He, too, must have remembered what a loser I was in high school. I will never forget a boy named

Rick who told me when I was fifteen years old that no boy in school wanted to date me. I was horrified when he said that in front of my girlfriends as I stood there, unable to defend myself. Didn't Jeff remember? Didn't he know? I tried to explain to Jeff why I thought he shouldn't be attracted to me.

Lucky for me, Jeff is a very patient and loving man.

The fact that Jeff knew me from a very awkward and painful period of my childhood brought out those insecurities that I had forgotten, buried deep, and not bothered to confront. So you see, I, too, thought I had moved on from my past when, in fact, I still carried it with me. We never know when something will show up to trigger emotions that we thought we had locked away in a box, hidden on the top shelf.

But when that box does spring open, having the tools that I'm sharing with you throughout this book will help you face what spills out and rebound quickly.

Your Turn

As a certified hypnotherapist, I see many clients looking to lose weight after experiencing strings of failures. Most have tried just about everything else that is available on the market to deal with their problem. In fact, I'm pretty much the last option when they do come to see me. This works in my favor—and theirs—because their desperation leaves them open to trying something they previously may not have thought would work. Most people tend to see hypnosis as something "out there" or a parlor game where someone is made to do silly things, such as cluck like a chicken or do an Elvis solo on stage. Although some people might find themselves on stage clucking away, no one can be hypnotized or made to do anything unless he or she wants to.

So before I begin any hypnosis, I spend time talking with the client. I need to make sure that he or she does want to change—to lose weight or stop smoking or overcome whatever problem the client has come to me to solve.

But most of my time with clients covers areas they never expected to address. Through both my own experience and that of clients I have helped over the years, I have found that those external issues cover up the real problems. And if we want truly to solve the obvious one, we must first address the deeper one, and that invariably revolves around self-love.

As I will with you, I help my clients to love themselves as they did many, many years ago. With that self-love once more intact, their prancing kitten bounces out, and they find they can accomplish anything. And so will you. Losing weight only begins your journey to a joyous, fulfilling life.

I must emphasize that this method deals with the positive in moving forward. Although we examine the past in depth, we do so to understand and not to blame. We leave no room for negativity, which would only hold us back from our heart's desire.

Remember when I told you I had gained fifty pounds, hated my job, left an abusive relationship, and moved in with my daughter? I had lost so much, but I still had what no one could take from me: the determination to climb out of my rut and do better.

That's where we all begin—with the decision to make this change. And then we do it, not just try to do it but actually do it by committing to following through on the three simple steps I will give you. I have done this, my clients have done this, and I know you can.

Let's get started.

Step 1: Face the Past

Few of us was had the benefits of a perfect upbringing, filled with unconditional love and support. Perhaps we encountered ridicule as a means of discipline. Maybe a parent never fully accepted us as the unique individual we are. And maybe the overall effect of our early years left us with deep feelings of doubt about our self-worth.

Yet, all of us come into this world innocent, full of love, and eager to learn. We depend totally upon our parents for our most basic needs, and we look to them to teach us how to make our way through life. As children, we have little control over what we are taught. If our parents tell us they love us and then hit us, we may get mixed signals about what love means.

Love hurts, we might think or, *Love comes with pain.* Or we might defend our parents and see ourselves as the cause of the pain, thinking, *My parents love me and wouldn't hurt me unless I am bad. I must be an awful person that they hurt me this way.*

Or maybe we encountered a situation outside our home that left deep emotional wounds. Sometimes continued sexual, physical, or emotional abuse pounds in the message that we deserve such treatment. We reason that we must be unworthy of love or we would never receive such pain.

Perhaps mean children targeted us as a child, and we felt no one could help us. A client I'll call Jackie was bullied as far back as she can remember in grade school. Not only did her classmates verbally abuse her, but they also knocked her books out of her hands almost every day for years.

Sometimes we hold a chance remark as evidence of our unworthiness. In a vulnerable state at the time, we misinterpreted or put undue weight upon another's words and let it grow until we believed it. As children—even as adults—we usually fail to understand that a person's negative words or actions reflect upon that person and not us. So we think, even with a lone "You're so stupid" that, indeed, we must be as the words say.

Few of us grow up without encountering such negativity in various forms. But not everyone carries those experiences with them throughout life, and those who love themselves let the negative go so that they have room for only love. That is what we will begin to do here.

But before we can bring love in, before we can love ourselves, we must rid ourselves of what keeps love out.

When I help my clients through hypnotherapy, we spend much time talking about this. I find that all of my clients have a story to share. Often they have buried it deep within or blocked it up and, in some way, refuse to let it out. And so it holds them back. It doesn't matter if they come to me for weight loss, smoking cessation, anxiety, or anything else; most of them have dealt with some kind of painful event that they are keeping to themselves, and it is keeping them from loving themselves and leading a joy-filled life. So getting that story out becomes our first job.

And so it will be with you. You have to get your story out. I don't mean that you should tell the world. In fact, spreading it that far may work against your best interests. For now, we just need to tell it. And since we're not having a private session where you can talk to me, you'll do the next best thing.

Write It Down

For your first step, set aside about at least an hour when you know no interruptions will intrude. A weekday evening often works best—everyone has finished eating and cleaning up, young children are sleeping, everyone else has settled down, calls have stopped, and you can relax.

Now, get out a pen and several sheets of paper. Write down everything bad that anyone ever said or did to you. Go far back to your very young days, and write down all the details of each instance. Continue on to the present.

Make sure you write this. Typing on a keyboard will not allow you to convey the emotions that a pen will. And writing, the physical movement of your hand on the paper, allows you greater expression than you get from predetermined fonts on a computer. So write by hand.

Take your time. Do this over several days to make sure you say all you must. You should record everything, and you may have some especially painful experiences buried so deeply that they need more time to rise up.

Be aware that some things we simply block out or we don't acknowledge how much they still bother us and affect our present life. In fact, we gain weight or do whatever rather than address the deeper issue because we don't want to face it. We would rather look awful—after all, that matches our (mis)perception of ourselves—than confront the real problem. We have carried that idea that we are not worthy for so long that we identify with it. *That is who I am*, we tell ourselves. *I can't change myself. I can't. I really can't.*

And an ugly little thought, often well hidden in the deep recesses of our mind, makes change that much harder. If we can change and we would change, what would that say about all of those years spent suffering in our overweight skin? What would it say about the opportunities we missed? What would it say about the life we let slip by? Could we tell ourselves that it was in vain, that we needn't have suffered, that we could have had those years as joy rather than as pain? Some of us would actually rather remain in misery and, somehow, justify the past by continuing to carry the pain into the present and future.

But the past is past. We cannot reclaim it. We can only live now. So we have the choice—to live in that familiar pain or to move into something different, a joyful existence. What we do here determines the choice we make. You have come this far because you sense that the past has not served you and you know you deserve better. You are ready to move forward, to let out what hurt you so that you can finally put it where it belongs, in the past.

As you record what happened, also think—and write—about your fears surrounding those events. What fears have you carried into the present? Are you afraid that love will hurt because it did decades ago? Are you afraid that if you lose the excess weight no one will love you? Or maybe someone actually will love you? Does your excess weight protect you? If so, from what? Your fear might stem from something that happened when you were a small child. It might be something that happened in school when you were a teenager. Or maybe something so traumatizing happened that you don't even remember it. This thing called "fear" connects in some way to your excess weight. Fear in one form or another stops all of us from moving forward in life and succeeding. And only we ourselves can undo the power fear has over us—by facing it, understanding it, and then moving on as we let love replace it.

Set a deadline of no more than three days to get everything down. You might miss something, but later you can go through this same process for that little bit. By keeping to the deadline, you avoid getting stuck in the muck of the past. Remember, you are doing this so you can get past the negativity that is holding you down. You can linger here only a short time.

At this time, your writing is for only you. You will not share it with anyone else.

Write down all the facts as you remember them. Record what a person said, where you were, how you felt, etc. But do not blame anyone—not you and not someone else. You are not finding fault here; you are finding the reasons for your feelings of unworthiness.

In Summary

Step 1: Face the Past

- Set aside an uninterruptible hour.

- Use pen and paper.

- Write details of every personal violation you experienced in your life.

- Face your fears and write them down.

- Complete it within three days.

Step 2: Transition

UNDERSTANDING

Just as you came into this world innocent, so did those who hurt you. Something, somewhere in their lives triggered a reaction that left such pain that they felt compelled to hurt others. Does this make their actions okay? NO! We are not excusing what they did but, instead, understanding that they, too, must have been suffering.

Understanding paves the way for you to let them go in whatever way works for you. And you must release them in some way, or you will continue to hold parts of the picture that portrays you as unworthy. Maybe you can forgive. Or maybe you can see the situation from a different angle.

You can readily label them "bad" and "the abuser," but that makes you the victim. Maybe you were, but you have moved into the present, and you no longer have need for that role. You are preparing for self-love.

We tend to resist this letting go, feeling that we are letting those who hurt us off the hook. We say, *They should face up to what they did, they should admit wrong, they should pay, they should ...* Maybe. But while we concentrate on what they should do—and are not doing—we keep ourselves stuck in that past situation. Every time we think of them and what they should do, we keep alive what they did to us. We relive those incidents over and over. So whom do we hurt in this? We hurt only ourselves. To free ourselves finally from those situations and the negative feelings they stir up, we must release those whom we feel hurt us.

I know this is difficult. In some situations, I could not forgive the person who hurt me, but I found another way to look at what happened, understand it from that perspective, and let go. You can do the same—to see differently and then release the past and embrace the now.

SANCTUARY

Only you know what you went through growing up. Even if you share your experiences with others, they cannot feel exactly what you felt nor know how you feel now.

Many of us have spent a lifetime protecting ourselves as best we know how from getting hurt again. We may feel vulnerable if we let go of those past hurts, as if by releasing them they can somehow come back to us. Holding onto their memory may serve as our only means of control, reminding us of the past so we won't put ourselves in the same situation again.

Regardless of the reason for not letting go, we must release the past. Because my clients often feel uncomfortable doing this, I help them create a safe haven so they can confidently let the pains of the past go away. I do this under hypnosis, but you can create a safe place in your mind on your own.

Find a quiet place at a time when you know you won't be disturbed. Sit down, relax, and close your eyes. Imagine a sanctuary where you will feel completely protected. In your mind, make it as specific as possible—where it is (a castle, a mountaintop, another planet, in the arms of a special person, etc.), what surrounds it, what stirs your senses (smells, sounds, temperature, light or dark), etc.

Now, see yourself as a child enter that special place, feeling safe and loved. Then, see your present self join your child-self.

This helps you understand that the child you once were is now safe. That child-self, who may have been harmed, teased, yelled at, or whatever, safely abides with your adult-self. When you allow yourself to see your inner child—so beautiful, so innocent, so playful—you begin to make room for joy to enter your life. No one can ever hurt your child-self again, and you feel free to let that part of you—your prancing kitten—out to play once more

Release the Past

Once you have found a way to release those who hurt you and have created a sanctuary safe from them for your inner child, you can physically release their hurtful actions.

Bring out all of those pages you wrote about what they did and how you felt and destroy them. Use whatever method you like—burn them, shred them, compost them, tear them into tiny pieces and scatter them to the wind, use them to line the bird cage and then toss them. Just make sure you completely rid yourself of them in a relatively short time.

In Summary

Step 2: Transition

- See those who hurt you as fellow humans who themselves were hurting.

- Release them; forgive them if you can.

- Create a sanctuary for your inner child.

- Destroy your written record of all they did to you.

Step 3: Face the Present

Congratulations! You've put the past in the only place it should be—behind you—and made room for today.

Now, it's time for you.

MIRROR, MIRROR ON THE WALL

I will now have you do one of the most difficult tasks ever asked of you: Tell yourself that you love you.

The first time I looked into the mirror to tell myself "I love you" was traumatic. I had just read the book, *You Can Heal Your Life*, by Louise L. Hay. One of her first assignments was for me to look into the mirror and tell myself, "I love you, Lisa." There was no way I wanted to look at myself in the mirror and say those words. At that time, I did not feel that way, and I certainly didn't want to look at myself and lie point-blank. There I stood that first time, looking in the mirror and seeing only wrinkles, gray hair growing out from the last hair dye, and a frown on my face. I could not even begin to utter the words, "Lisa, I love you." I simply stood there and cried.

I can't tell you how long I faced that bathroom mirror—one minute or, perhaps, ten. Nor can I tell you how many tissues my teary eyes went through. But ... I did it. I stood there, looking back at my red, puffy face with mascara running down, sniffling as I finally said, "Lisa, I love you."

When I finished, I felt numb. I thought to myself, "Why was that so difficult? I have no trouble telling other people around me that I love them, yet I couldn't say it to myself. What is wrong with me?"

Despite my hard-won success that first day, I wanted to block out the assignment I had given myself—to do this for two straight weeks to see if I could look at myself without crying or feeling guilty. Thank heavens for sticky notes so I could put one on my mirror and see it when I was brushing my teeth and have no excuse not to remember.

At first, I didn't notice a difference when I repeated the words. I had such a difficult time making eye contact with the person looking back in the mirror that I even tried putting on my make-up first, thinking that would make a difference in how I felt about myself. It didn't. It took several days of looking into the mirror and repeating those words, and then it finally hit me. How can I expect others to love me if I cannot love myself? If I can't look into the mirror and love the person looking back at me, how can I expect anyone else to? That's when I realized that loving ourselves is necessary if we truly want to be loved by others. And if we don't like what we see in the mirror, then it's time to figure out why.

Your turn.

Look into the mirror and say your name, followed by, "I love you. What good can I do for you today?" I tell my clients to do this assignment right after they brush their teeth in the morning. That way, they do it first thing in the morning and make it a daily routine.

If you can, let a person you love and trust know what you are doing and tell him or her how you do each day for the first two weeks. If possible, this person can go through the same process, and you each can be accountable to the other during this time.

The Golden Halo

You've now set the stage for positive change to enter your life. You've rid yourself of thoughts and feelings of unworthiness and replaced them with self-love. And when you love yourself, you will naturally take good care of you. Don't you do that with everyone else—for those you love and care for? You prepare healthy meals for them, nurse them when sick, give reminders that you love them, etc. Don't you deserve the same? You love you, so now you can care for you and show you that you love you.

Begin with food. When I work with clients wanting to lose weight, I give them a non-surgical lap-band under hypnosis. A surgical lap-band keeps a person from eating more than a very small portion of food at a time by restricting how much the stomach can hold. My method saves the client the time, expense, and risks of surgery while providing the same benefit of limiting food consumption.

I call this non-surgical lap-band applied under hypnosis a "golden halo." It works on my clients, and it worked on me. That fifty pounds I mentioned that I gained in two years I lost in eight months without consciously dieting; I just ate less because I had "told" my subconscious that I could eat only a little at a time.

HYPNOSIS WORKS

Our subconscious exerts considerable control over what we do and how we think. If we can harness it and bring that control into our awareness, then our behavior will reflect a consistency between our subconscious and conscious mind.

Most people think that our conscious mind determines our actions, but we use only 12 percent of our mind consciously. Ideally, we use this part of the mind for making important decisions. Too often, though, we use it for lesser and, unfortunately, hurtful analyses—judging others, labeling, criticizing, etc.

The other 88 percent of our mind consists of our subconscious, unconscious, and super-conscious. This means that we may act counter to what we consciously want to do—such as indulge in desserts every day when we have sworn to consume sweets only on weekends—because our subconscious has reasons for us to do otherwise. And our subconscious, working behind the scenes where we cannot see it, keeps the upper hand in any battle with the conscious mind.

If you have failed in shedding extra pounds or freeing yourself from a defeating habit, your subconscious has likely stood in your way—without your realizing it. Wouldn't you like to get your subconscious working with you and not against you? While you may have tried other diets or read other self-help books, this book addresses why we think the way we do and how to make sure our actions reflect our conscious desires.

Hypnosis allows you to take control of your subconscious so it operates in harmony with your conscious. And hypnosis does work. As published in the *Journal of Consulting and Clinical Psychology*, researchers at the University of Connecticut analyzed eighteen studies, comparing a cognitive behavioral therapy—such as relaxation training, guided imagery, self-monitoring, or goal-setting—with the same therapy supplemented by hypnosis.

Those who received the hypnosis lost more weight than 90 percent of those not receiving hypnosis and maintained the weight loss two years after treatment ended.

As these and other studies indicate, hypnosis brings about the effects you consciously want. My personal experience confirms this as well, as does my hypnotherapy practice over the past eight years. I have consistently found that my clients achieve long-term success in overcoming self-defeating habits—finally, after years of failures.

Having a certified hypnotherapist guide you through the process makes the procedure easy and ensures thoroughness. But you can do the same on your own and at your convenience with hypnotherapy CDs. (See the Appendix for more information.)

EAT LESS, EAT WELL

Since we can't do hypnosis with you now, we use a trick to help you eat less. Brian Wansick, in his book, *Mindless Eating*, explains why we eat more than we think. It's well worth the read to understand just how much we are sold on what others tell us is the correct thing. He mentions that standard dinner plate sizes have increased 36 percent since the 1960s, from a ten-inch plate to a twelve-inch plate. Since people tend to fill a plate, regardless of its size, "the amount people serve themselves goes up about 22 percent" with our current, larger dinner plate.

We have become a nation of super-sized and free refills to get the full-meal deal. We are suckered each and every day. I work with my clients to assist them in taking back their lives and changing the focus from food as a comfort and to food as a fuel. Many of us no longer sit at the table and have dinner with others but, instead, cram food in our mouths while watching our favorite show or while on the run. We don't even take the time to appreciate the taste and texture of the food we are eating after the first few bites. We simply shovel away.

As we all know, a key to losing weight is to eat less. But no one likes to deny him- or herself, so now we will trick ourselves into eating less without feeling denied. Rather than using a dinner plate (contemporary size or even the smaller, older one), we use a nine-inch salad plate for dinner. No need to count calories, fix special meals, or put lonely portions on a big plate. You can eat what everyone else does and feel you're getting a regular size meal because your plate will be full.

By applying the non-surgical lap-band and eating on the smaller plate, my clients notice a difference right away. And you will, too, with just the smaller plate portions. The guilt has been removed, and the focus is no longer on counting calories but, instead, on enjoying the family meal.

Also, as I tell my clients, if you are a late-night eater, you must put those late-night snacks on your salad plate with your dinner because you don't get to come back for seconds. If you want cookies, they must go on that salad plate for you to eat later. Your subconscious "sees" the full plate and reacts accordingly, thinking, *That's a lot. I'm going to feel stuffed.* In fact, by seeing the snacks mixed with dinner, your mind may react differently and not even desire the cookies after they have sat on the plate for several hours.

With the shift off the science of food—number of calories, nutritional content, portion size—you can relax. Set the stage for a quieter meal that encourages slow eating. Turn off the TV, light some candles, put on soothing music. And converse with others while you savor the food. Take your time and encourage sharing what happened during the day. As you talk and listen, you'll focus on the family or others with you, and whether you still have food on your plate or not will no longer matter. What others are saying will. Meals will become a pleasurable experience for everyone.

Show That You Love You

Your body is your temple. How you treat it reflects how you feel about yourself. Eating properly shows you care enough about you to feed yourself nutritious, well-balanced meals of moderate portions.

But loving yourself goes beyond the food you eat. Think about your physical appearance. Which does it say: "I don't care" or "I love me"? Sweats might work for painting a room, but they otherwise say, "Please just ignore me. Don't see me. I don't really matter." The alternative is not necessarily dressing to the nines. You know what to do to look as if you care about you—clean, neat, hair in place, clothes that fit, a little jewelry, and some sparkle. Add a dash of color or a snazzy accessory. I'll bet you did this years ago. And if not, why not now?

When you care about you, you'll want—yes, *want*—to get and stay in shape with exercise. As you shed pounds, you will find physical activity easier and enjoyable. You'll want to walk in the woods, you'll thrill to notch up the weights you're lifting, you'll take pride in your toned body. And, yes, it will come. Not overnight. But you know that, just as you now know not to place unrealistic expectations in front of yourself that will only defeat you.

You love yourself. What good are you going to do for yourself today?

In Summary

Step 3: Face the Present

- Look in the mirror and tell yourself, "_____, I love you. What good can I do for you today?"

- Put dinner and any late-night snacks on a nine-inch salad plate.

- Relax and make eating enjoyable, concentrating on socializing.

- Take care of your body.

Loving Life

When you love yourself, others will follow suit. You believe you are worthy, and you will project out that feeling, in effect giving others permission to see you as lovable.

And then the magic begins.

You've shifted to the upward spiral. When you love yourself, others respond to your attitude about yourself. That validates your self-love, which increases your good feelings. You, then, give out those even stronger good feelings about yourself, to which others, again, respond in a positive way. And so it continues, onward, upward, love for yourself, for others, for life itself, ever growing.

Now what?

You Can Do Anything

Before, although you held the negative past in your mind, it manifested in your body as excess weight or other self-destructive habits. Ridding yourself of that past removes a tremendous and weighty burden from your psyche as well as from your physical body. In its place, you will find a power-surge of energy in your life.

Challenges will continue to come your way. How will you respond? Will you see them as barriers and turn back in fear? Or will you see them as opportunities to learn and grow and move forward? We always have those two choices—one based on fear and one based on love.

Fear stands in yesterday, reminding you of past failings, mistakes, feelings of inadequacy. It surrounds you in negativity and keeps you stuck in that past. Fear tells you to doubt yourself, to look to others to save you, to believe you can't really do anything.

Love tells you the opposite. Self-love forms the foundation for all other forms of positive, life-affirming energy—joy, peace, happiness, initiative, respect, love of others, etc. When you love yourself, you realize you can do anything you set your mind to do. To accomplish your goal, you draw upon your belief in yourself: "I love me. I can do anything." These statements are centered in now, in today, and have no relationship to the past. In this very moment, you hold the power to get done what you must to meet your challenges.

You may do so in one grand sweep, or you may need many steps to reach your ultimate goal. No matter. You believe in that wonderful, powerful you, and you will take the time you must as you continue to get closer to it.

As you move forward in love, you will find you attract other people of love who will support you. Beyond a partner or family members, mentors will enter your life, returning to you the love you are sending out and now building up. As they help and guide you, you will, in turn, give out your guidance to others. This feels so good—giving out love in such a form and seeing it spread.

And where did it begin? With you and "_____, I love you."

Your Purpose

You used to put so much energy just in coping that you had little left for anything beyond the everyday duties—fixing meals, working, doing the chores, getting the children organized, off, and then back home again. You faced each day in survival mode, hoping only to get through it so you could make it to bed, get up the next day, and do the same all over again. You had no resources within you for much else. A purpose in life? Just get through this day, please.

And now, as energy pours into you, as you attract loving people into your life, as the good flows to you, you find you can think beyond the mundane. You realize you have a reason for being here besides mere existence.

Each of us has a purpose in this life. And now, you have the emotional resources to consider yours. What are you going to do? How will you get it done? Whose help will you enlist? How is that prancing kitten inside of you doing? Eager to get out and show the world what you can do?

BE YOUR OWN HERO

To tell ourselves that we love ourselves has nothing to do with ego, conceit, or vanity. It's about pure, unconditional love. How can we possibly expect anyone to love us if we can't love ourselves? Ask yourself that question right now. All of our insecurities come from ourselves. Why do we need validation from others to tell us we are good enough? Why do we need to hear "I love you" from those we love? Shouldn't the fact that they are there in our lives be good enough? Just by being there—sharing our ups and downs, joys and sorrows—shows they care about us. Yet we think we need to hear words from them that really should be coming from ourselves.

No one is perfect, we hear throughout life. And yet we are our own worst enemy when it comes to judgment of ourselves and being happy with who we are, imperfections and all. Loving ourselves is mandatory for us to have a healthy, normal life. By changing our thinking of how we feel about ourselves, we change our entire outlook on life and take the first steps toward creating a life that we truly want.

Mentors flow through our lives. Partners may come and then go. Family members have their own lives to lead, their own paths to follow. Whom can you turn to when the chips are down? No matter your stage in life, you can always count on one person to be there for you: you.

You have amazing power. Sure, you have a network of friends and family to support you and offer advice, but when it comes to making any choice that affects your life, you get the right answers only from within. Listen to your heart. It knows where you need to go, what you need to accomplish.

I have given you the keys to turn your life around so you can be happy and wake up each morning ready to take on the world. But it will happen only if you do the work. I challenge you for two weeks to look into the mirror and say those words: "_____, I love you. What good can I do for you today?" See how you feel at the end of those two weeks. See how things actually start to look and feel just by doing that simple exercise.

I wish you only love and enjoyment in finding your own happiness. Remember that we were all born into this world innocent. May peace be your guide to happiness. Every day, love the person looking back at you in the mirror. Treat that person well for he or she is the most important person you will ever meet in this lifetime.

Appendix

Hypnosis

After seeing Dr. Bruce Goldberg perform hypnosis live in a television studio, I was very interested in the concept of tapping into the subconscious to change our own behavior. I studied this form of healing and became a certified hypnotherapist.

As I mentioned in this book, a person cannot be hypnotized unless he or she wants to. Yet misperceptions about hypnosis persist in most people's minds, keeping them from benefiting from this method of healing.

Hypnosis is a very relaxing experience. I tell my clients I am their tour guide, taking them on a pleasant journey where everything goes according to plan. The clients simply lie on a bed with their eyes closed as I talk to them.

MY HYPNOTHERAPY WORK

Before I begin a session with a client, I have the person fill out an intake form, similar to what doctors have patients complete before a medical examination. The questions on my form deal with clients' medical history, the reason for wanting to see me, how long they have had the problem they want to change (for example, smoking since a teenager).

In our session, I go over the form with the client, using the written responses to key me into further questions to ask. My goal is to hear the full story about the issue at hand. For instance, with a client wishing to lose weight, I learn not only the dieting history but also the client's relationship with food and eating, his or her attitude toward life, self-image, traumatic experiences, fears, personal relationships, and more. We spend almost two hours in discussion, and I make a point of letting my client take his or her time to talk without feeling rushed. Invariably, seemingly unrelated events or feelings—ones the client finally has a chance to share with someone—come out that actually impact the issue we are focusing on. So this time for talking becomes critical in the healing process.

Toward the end of the session, we do the hypnosis. I describe each step of the process that I will do in hypnotherapy so there are no surprises. If a person doesn't trust the hypnotherapist, it will not work.

Similar to the steps in this book, I then ask my clients to describe a sanctuary in which they would feel safe. It can be any place—real or imaginary—as long as it allows them to relax completely. Then I guide them through hypnosis.

I have my clients visualize being in the chosen sanctuary and lying down. Then, I "put on" the golden halo, which is the imaginary lap-band. I explain that the golden halo lap-band is not painful but they will feel a slight tugging the first few days, just like the feeling of a belt on a pair of pants tightening around their waist.

Next, I make positive statements about the future they will have with these changes and help them see what that by visualizing themselves looking into a full-length mirror and seeing themselves at their ideal weight. By allowing themselves to see what they will look like in the near future, they get excited to begin their journey. Then, I bring them to full awareness.

When I have finished my session with each client, I explain the importance of eating on a luncheon sized plate from now on for all meals. They cannot have seconds, and if they want any late-night snacks, they must be put onto the single-serving, dinner-meal lunch plate.

The hypnosis lap-band loosens up after about a week, so the client usually needs reinforcement through either more sessions with me directly or with one of my CDs. So, with weight loss, the number of sessions my clients need depends on how much weight they want to lose. I have all clients text me daily the first two weeks to report doing their "mirror work." But if they need to lose more then twenty-five pounds, I see them once a week for the first month. I also give them a custom CD to listen to at home. After that, I see them as needed, typically once or twice a month.

Most of my clients who want to quit smoking need only one session, but I have them schedule a second one in one week in case they need a follow-up session.

WHAT TO LOOK FOR IN A HYPNOTHERAPIST

I work in the Seattle/Puget Sound area of Washington State. You can find hypnotherapists throughout the US. In looking for one near you, make sure the person has certification from the state in which he or she is practicing. Ask about fees and any up-front charges. You should get a free initial consultation. And make sure to check the hypnotherapist's Website and ask for referrals.

Visit my Website to order hypnotherapy CDs:

www.LisaLamont.com